Disney
PRINCESS

Follow Your Dreams

PRINCESS3242

Code is valid for your Disney Princess ebook and may be redeemed through the Disney Story Central app on the App Store. Content subject to availability. Parent permission required. Code expires on December 31, 2019.

PaRragon

Bath · New York · Cologne · Melbourne · Delhi
Hong Kong · Shenzhen · Singapore

Undersea Search

Ariel loves to search for undersea treasures, but right now she is looking for Flounder! Help the Little Mermaid find her friend by tracing the correct path through the maze.

start

finish

Super
searching!
Give yourself
a sticker.

2

Answer on page 31

Naveen in Green

Tiana and Naveen go on a bayou adventure!
Color in the princess and her frog friend.
Make sure you use lots of green!

Well done!
Have a reward
sticker.

Royal Word Search

Merida loves to ride with Angus in the forest. Can you find the name ANGUS seven times in the grid below? Look up, down, forward, and backward.

N	A	G	A	N	S	N
A	N	G	U	S	U	A
N	G	A	G	S	G	N
G	U	S	N	G	N	G
U	S	U	G	N	A	U
S	U	G	N	A	U	S

You deserve a reward sticker!

4

Answers on page 31

Princess Pets

Jasmine, Cinderella, and Mulan are looking
for some of their favorite furry friends.
Help them by drawing a line from
each princess to her animal friend.

Paw-fect!
Give yourself a
reward sticker.

Answers on page 31

Which Path?

Genie is ready for a vacation,
but he wants to say good-bye to
Aladdin and Jasmine before he leaves.
Help him find them by tracing the right path.

Fantastic!
Give yourself
a reward
sticker.

6

Answer on page 31

Shadow Match

Maximus is always there for Rapunzel when she needs him! Find and circle the shadow that is an exact match of the picture of Rapunzel and her animal friend.

a

b

c

d

Did you find it? Place your reward sticker here.

Answer on page 31

Dancing Duo

Ariel uses her human legs
to dance with Eric. Can you spot
three things that are missing from
the picture on the opposite page?

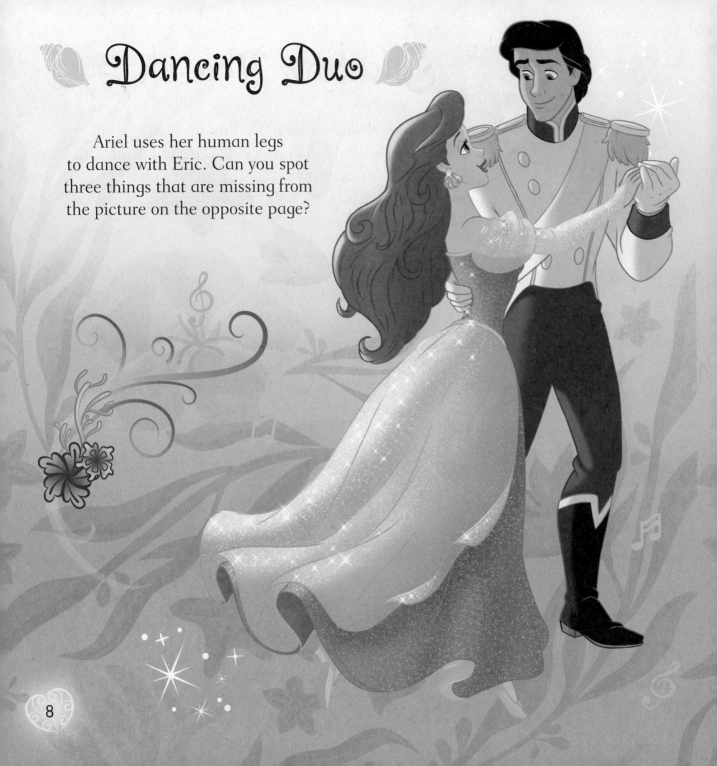

Add the missing items, and then color in the picture.

Great job! Have a reward sticker.

Ready for the Ball

Cinderella is ready for the ball. Connect the dots to make sure her dress looks perfect, and then color in the picture.

Give yourself a reward sticker!

Answer on page 31

Which Fairy Is Which?

How well do you know the Three Good Fairies?
Draw lines to match each fairy to her name.

Flora

Fauna

Merryweather

Clues:
Each fairy wears a different color: red, blue, or green.
Flora does not wear blue.
Merryweather does not wear green.

Did you match them all? Have a reward sticker!

Answers on page 31

11

Spot the Differences

Rapunzel has long golden hair!
Take a good look at the pictures,
then find and circle three
differences between the two.

You deserve
a reward
sticker!

12

Answers on page 31

Tiana's Treat

Tiana is cooking herself a perfect meal.
She hopes it will be delicious enough
to serve at her new restaurant!
Help her cook by drawing lines
from the food items to their
correct places in the picture.

Nice work!
Give yourself a
reward sticker.

13

Answers on page 31

Shall We Dance?

Ariel thinks Sebastian is the perfect dance partner! If you were going to a royal ball, who would your dance partner be? Draw a picture of yourself and your perfect partner below!

Nice picture! Now add your reward sticker.

Tweet, Tweet!

Snow White loves to sing along
with the birds in the forest!
How many birds can you count
in this picture?

Did you count
them all?
You deserve a
reward sticker!

Answer on page 31

15

Copy and Color!

Help Mrs. Potts get ready for tea!
Using the grid, copy the picture of
Mrs. Potts and then color her in.

Tea-rific!
Give yourself a
reward sticker.

Tweet, Tweet!

Snow White loves to sing along with the birds in the forest! How many birds can you count in this picture?

Did you count them all? You deserve a reward sticker!

15

Answer on page 31

Copy and Color!

Help Mrs. Potts get ready for tea!
Using the grid, copy the picture of
Mrs. Potts and then color her in.

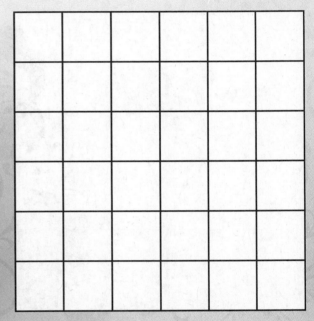

Tea-rific!
Give yourself a
reward sticker.

16

Reward Stickers

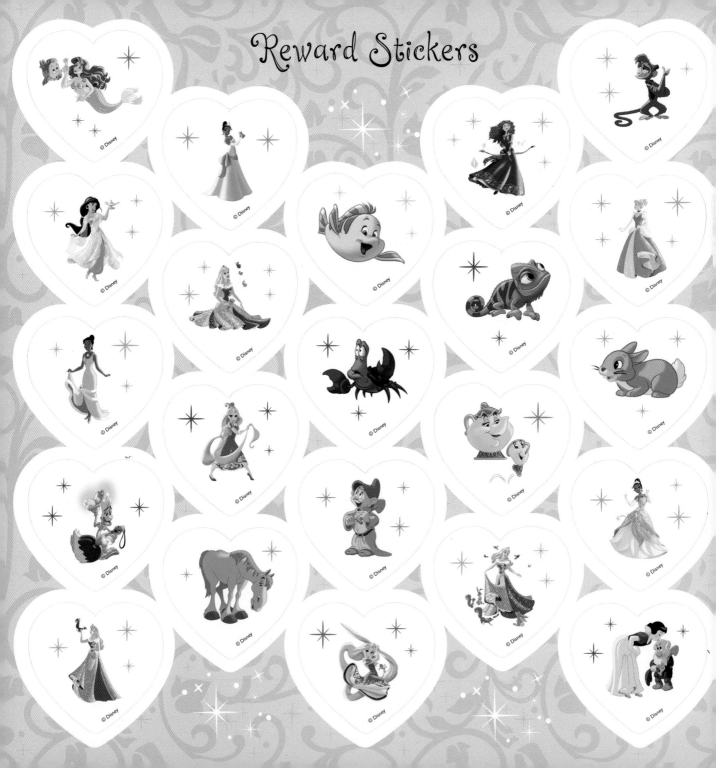

Just for Fun!

Cinderella's Special Day

Cinderella has a big day ahead of her, and it just might involve a royal ball. Read all about it below. Draw a line between each picture and the place it belongs in the story.

It is time to go to the ball, but Cinderella has nothing to wear! Then her ⬜ appears. She waves her wand and creates a ⬜ for Cinderella to ride to the ⬜.

But Cinderella must be careful and watch the ⬜ so she can get home before midnight.

clock

castle

fairy godmother

coach

Did you finish the story? Give yourself a sticker!

17

Answers on page 32

Tiana's Tea Party

Tiana is baking for a special party for her friends, and she wants everything to be perfect. Can you help her decorate? Color the correct number of cupcakes for her special guests.

5 for
Big Daddy

2 for
Eudora

3 for
Charlotte

Wonderful!
Now add your
reward sticker.

A-mazing Date!

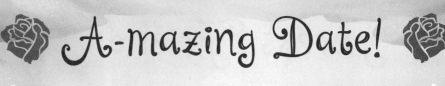

Belle and the Beast are having a skating date!
Help Belle get to the Beast by finding
the right path through the maze.

start

finish

You deserve
a reward
sticker!

19

Forest Friends

Snow White has lots of friends in
the forest. Draw lines to match each
animal in the picture to its name.

chipmunks

raccoon

bunny

bird

Nice work!
Place your
reward sticker
here.

20

Answers on page 32

Dream It, Do It!

Ever since she was a little girl, Rapunzel has dreamed of going on an adventure to see the floating lights. What's your big dream for the future? Draw or write it below!

Now add your reward sticker!

Where's Aurora?

The good fairies are eager to find Princess Aurora
so they can enjoy afternoon tea together.
Help them find her by decoding the puzzle below.

start

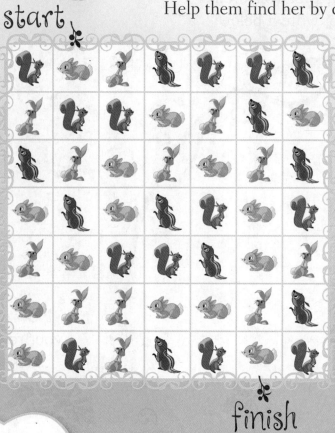

finish

up

left

down

right

 22

You deserve
a reward
sticker!

Answer on page 32

Merida's Mix-Up

Harris, Hamish, and Hubert are playing games
with Merida by hiding in different places.
She has counted five little brothers, but she
only has three! Help her out by spotting which
brothers have appeared twice.

a

c

b

d

e

Answers on page 32

Give yourself
a reward
sticker!

23

Beautiful Butterflies

Meeko loves butterflies,
but there are too many for
him to play with!
How many butterflies do
you count?

Add your
reward sticker
here!

24

Answer on page 32

Oh Brother!

Mulan is looking for Little Brother,
but he's still too busy running in circles!
Help Little Brother get to Mulan by
tracing the right path for him.

a

b

c

Did you find
the right path?
Have a reward
sticker!

Answer on page 32

25

A Party for a Prince!

It's almost Prince Phillip's birthday,
and Aurora wants to make it extra special.
Can you help her prepare?

How many wrapped gifts do you count? _____

How many cupcakes do you count? _____

Who else is hiding in the picture?

_____

Place your
reward sticker
here.

26

Answers on page 32

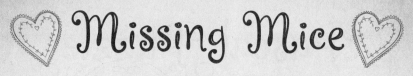

Missing Mice

Cinderella is kind to all animals—especially her loyal mice pals!
Spot and circle all nine mice hiding in the picture below.

Give yourself
a royal reward
sticker.

Pascal Puzzle

Pascal has changed colors so many times, he's even confused himself! Help him get organized by making sure each color of Pascal appears only once in each row and column. Write the correct letter in each empty box.

A

B

C

D

Perfect! Give yourself a reward sticker.

28

Answers on page 32

Make a Splash!

Ariel jumps above water whenever she can!
Only two of these pictures are exactly alike.
Can you spot them? When you do, draw
a big heart around each one.

a   b   c

d   e

Did you find the
matching pictures?
Have a reward
sticker!

Answer on page 32

29

Picture Perfect

Can you help the princesses look picture perfect?
One of the pictures in each row is different from the
other two. Find and circle the odd one out in each row.

Nice work!
Now add your
reward sticker.

Answers on page 32

Answers

Page 2

start

finish

Page 4

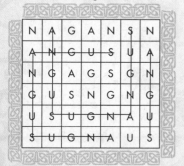

Page 5

Page 6

Path c leads to Aladdin and Jasmine

Page 7

Shadow d is a match

Pages 8-9

Page 10

Page 11

Flora wears red
Fauna wears green
Merryweather wears blue

Page 12

Page 13

Page 15

There are 6 birds

Page 17

It is time to go to the ball, but Cinderella has nothing to wear! Then her ☐ appears. She waves her wand and creates a ☐ for Cinderella to ride to the ☐. But Cinderella must be careful and watch the ☐ so she can get home before midnight.

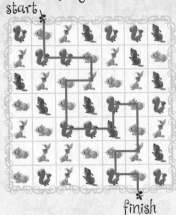

Page 19

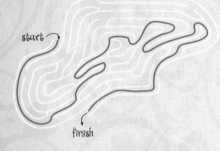

start

finish

Page 20

chipmunks

raccoon

bunny

bird

Page 22

start

finish

Page 23

a and b are the same
c and d are the same
e appears only once

Page 24

There are 7 butterflies

Page 25

Path b leads Little Brother to Mulan

Page 26

There are 4 wrapped gifts
There are 4 cupcakes
King Stefan is hiding

Page 27

Page 28

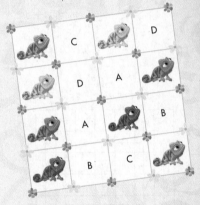

Page 29

b and e are the same

Page 30

The odd ones out are:
row 1–b; row 2–a, row 3–c